125 Easy to Use Oral Activities

Written by
Thomas Alsop

Managing Editor
Ryan West

Page Layout Artist
Melissa Woodington

ISBN: 978-0-7560-0412-5
SKU: B1380
Printed in Roseville, MI • 1006GRA

ALSOP

FOR THE TEACHER

OVERVIEW

There are twenty-six chapters covering vocabulary and grammar. Students talk about themselves and others, sing and describe visuals, while focusing on the vocabulary or grammar concept in the chapter. There is a grading rubric to facilitate oral test evaluation. The entire book is in Spanish.

HOW TO

1. Make copies of the topic you select. There are two pages and five parts to each topic.
2. The students follow the instructions for each part, and complete that activity in the time allotted. Students work at their seats, in pairs or groups of four. In the *Toda la clase-De pie* section, students stand and walk about the room while speaking with each other.
3. Students first practice the oral activities with each other in groups.
4. Use the rubric to help grade the students.
5. Keep the tempo of the class moving, students speak Spanish for fifty minutes! Play music in Spanish on a CD player to add authenticity to the setting.

TIME

The entire two page assignment will take 50 minutes to complete.

ALSOP

INDEX

ALSOP

Rubric-50 points possible-
10 points for each category

47-50-Outstanding
42-46-Very Good
38-41-Good
34-37-Average
30-33-Weak
Below 30-Failing

Student	Pronunciation	Fluency	Vocab	Grammar	Creativity/ Enthusiasm

ALSOP

Nombre: ___________________________

Fecha: ____________________________

Hora: _____________________________

Saludos

Parte 1-En parejas-6 minutos
Take turns. Introduce yourself. Say your name. Greet your friend. Ask his/her name and find out how he/she is.
Use these clues: ***llamarse, cómo, estar.***

Parte 2-Toda la clase-De pie-12 minutos
Take turns. Introduce yourself to each member of class. Say your name. Greet your friends. Ask each student his/her name and how he/she is.
Use these clues: ***llamarse, cómo, buenos días, buenas tardes, cómo, estar.***

Parte 3-En parejas-6 minutos
Take turns giving a short speech sin which you say, your name, how you are, and any other pertinent information.
Use these clues: ***llamarse, estar, bien, mal, nervioso(a), triste, cansado.***

Parte 4-En grupos de cuatro-14 minutos
Take turns. Role-play a celebrity movie star or singer. Say your name and how you are. Add any other information you can.
Use these clues: ***llamarse, cómo, estar, bien, contento(a), entusiasmado(a).***

ALSOP

 www.teachersdiscovery.com

Saludos

Nombre: ______________________

Fecha: ______________________

Hora: ______________________

Parte 5-En parejas. ¿Qué dices?-12 minutos

1. Take turns. Look at the drawing below. Invent a name for each person or animal. Then use these cues to say how person is. Use these clues: ***llamarse, está triste, cansada, contento(a), enfermo(a), enojados, triste.*** Say two sentences in Spanish for each drawing.

1.

2.

3.

4.

5.

6.

ALSOP

Los objetos de clase

Nombre: ____________________

Fecha: ____________________

Hora: ____________________

Parte 1-En parejas-6 minutos
Take turns saying as many classroom objects as possible.
Point to them while saying their names.
Use some of these clues: ***es, son, pizarra, tiza, borrador, pupitre, mesa, ventana, luces.***

Parte 2-Toda la clase-De pie-14 minutos
Take turns. Introduce yourself and tell each student four classroom objects. Point to each one while speaking.
Use some of these clues: ***reloj, pizarra, libros, mapa, bandera, puerta.***

Parte 3-En parejas-6 minutos
Take turns saying the classroom objects as fast as you can. Point while saying the objects.
Use some of these clues: ***es, sones, pizarra, tiza, borrador, pupitre, mesa, ventana, luces.***

Parte 4-En grupos de cuatro-14 minutos
Make a short rap song using four of the classroom objects. Sing your song
Use some of these clues: ***es, son, pizarra, tiza, borrador, pupitre, mesa, ventana, luces, libros, mapa, bandera, puerta, carteles.***

Los objetos de clase

Nombre: ______________________

Fecha: ______________________

Hora: ______________________

Parte 5-En parejas. ¿Qué dices?-10 minutos

1. Look at the drawing below. Describe the classroom objects and people in Sra. Moreno's classroom. Say two sentences in Spanish for each drawing.
Use some of these clues: ***hay, bandera, lápiz, muchacho, profesora, pupitre, sillas, bandera, sacapuntas, pizarra, borrador, hay, sol, arco iris, México, libros, tiza.***

1.

2.

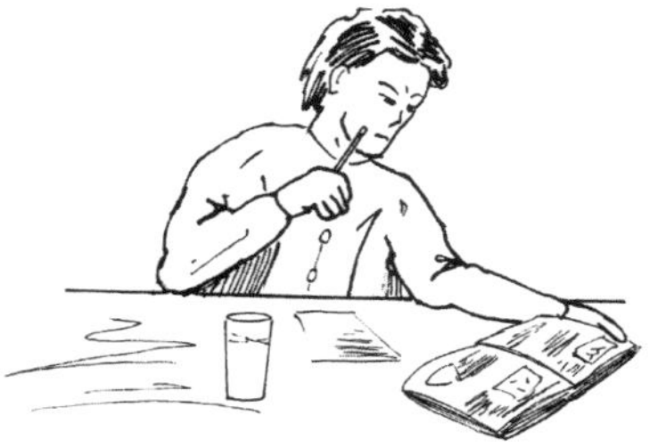

3.

4.

5.

6.

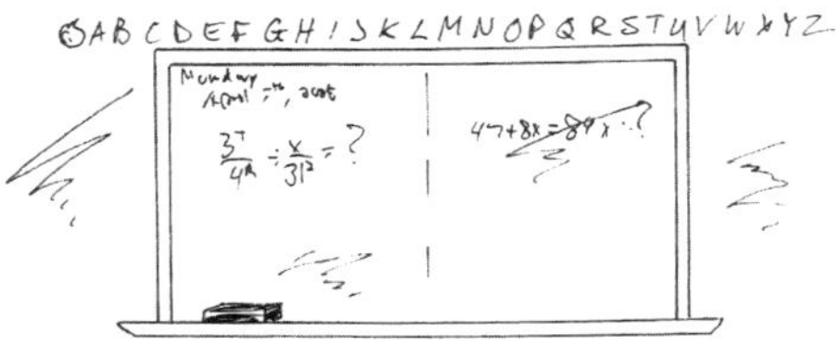

ALSOP

Los verbos AR

Nombre: ______________________

Fecha: ______________________

Hora: ______________________

Parte 1-En parejas-6 minutos
Take turns asking the other if he/she: speaks Spanish,
studies English, works a lot, listens to the radio, and prepares the meal.
Use these clues: ***hablar, estudiar, trabajar, escuchar, preparar.***

Parte 2-Toda la clase-De pie-14 minutos
Take turns. Tell each class member what you do using an AR verb. For example: *hablo español, preparo la comida*, etc. Use at least three different AR verbs while speaking.
Use some of these clues: ***mirar, practicar, visitar, viajar, hablar.***

Parte 3-En parejas-8 minutos
Take turns. You role-play a famous celebrity. Give a short speech saying what you do. Use at least four AR verbs.
Use some of these clues: ***hablar, estudiar, trabajar, escuchar, preparar.***

Parte 4-En grupos de cuatro-12 minutos
Make a short rock song using the endings of one AR verb. Sing your song.
For example: *hablar-yo hablo, tú hablas, él, ella, Ud. habla, nosotros halamos, vosotros habláis, ellos, Uds. hablan.*
Use one of these clues: ***trabajar, cantar, bailar.***

Los verbos AR

Nombre: ____________________

Fecha: ____________________

Hora: ____________________

Parte 5-En parejas. ¿Qué dices?-10 minutos

1. Take turns Look at the drawing below. Describe what the people are doing. Say two sentences in Spanish for each drawing. Use some of these clues: ***trabajar, hablar, escuchar, mirar, viajar, practicar.***

1.

2.

3.

4.

5.

6.

ALSOP

Los verbos ER

Nombre: ______________________

Fecha: ______________________

Hora: ______________________

Parte 1-En parejas-6 minutos
Take turns asking the other if he/she: eats a lot, learns Spanish, runs in the park, reads at home, and drinks coffee.
Use these clues: ***comer, aprender, correr, leer, beber.***

Parte 2-Toda la clase-De pie-14 minutos
Take turns. Tell each class member what you do using an ER verb. For example: *como en casa, aprendo mucho,* etc. Use at least three different ER verbs while speaking.
Use some of these clues: ***comer, prometer, correr, leer, esconder.***

Parte 3-En parejas-8 minutos
Take turns. You role-play a famous celebrity. Give a short speech saying what you do. Use at least four ER verbs.
Use some of these clues: ***aprender, correr, ver, leer, comer, beber.***

Parte 4-En grupos de cuatro-12 minutos
Make a short rap song using the endings of one ER verb. Sing your song
For example: *comer–yo como, tú comes, él, ella, Ud. come, nosotros comemos, vosotros/as coméis, ellos/as, Uds. comen.*
Use one of these clues: ***aprender, correr, comer.***

ALSOP

Los verbos ER

Nombre: ______________________

Fecha: ______________________

Hora: ______________________

Parte 5-En parejas. ¿Qué dices?-10 minutos

1. Take turns Look at the drawing below. Describe what the people are doing. Say two sentences in Spanish for each drawing. Use some of these clues: ***correr, comer, beber, aprender, leer, ver.***

1.

2.

3.

4.

5.

6.

ALSOP

Los verbos IR

Nombre: ______________________

Fecha: ______________________

Hora: ______________________

Parte 1-En parejas-6 minutos
Take turns asking the other if he/she: writes letters, lives in Mexico, opens the door, and decides tomorrow.
Use these clues: ***escribir, vivir, abrir, decidir, subir.***

Parte 2-Toda la clase-De pie-14 minutos
Take turns. Tell each class member what you do using an IR verb. For example: *escribo cartas, vivo en España*, etc. Use at least three different IR verbs while speaking.
Use some of these clues: ***subir, recibir, partir, abrir, escribir.***

Parte 3-En parejas-8 minutos
Take turns. You role-play a famous celebrity. Give a short speech saying what you do. Use at least four IR verbs.
Use some of these clues: ***recibir, vivir, escribir, partir, dividir.***

Parte 4-En grupos de cuatro-12 minutos
Make a short love song using the endings of one IR verb. Sing your song.
For example: *partir-yo parto, tú partes, él, ella, Ud. parte, nosotros partimos, vosotros/as partís, ellos/as, Uds. parten.*
Use one of these clues: ***vivir, subir, escribir.***

ALSOP

Los verbos IR

Nombre: ____________________

Fecha: ____________________

Hora: ____________________

Parte 5-En parejas. ¿Qué dices?-10 minutos

1. Take turns Look at the drawing below. Describe what the people are doing. Say two sentences in Spanish for each drawing. Use some of these clues: ***vivir, escribir, subir, partir, recibir, abrir.***

1.

2.

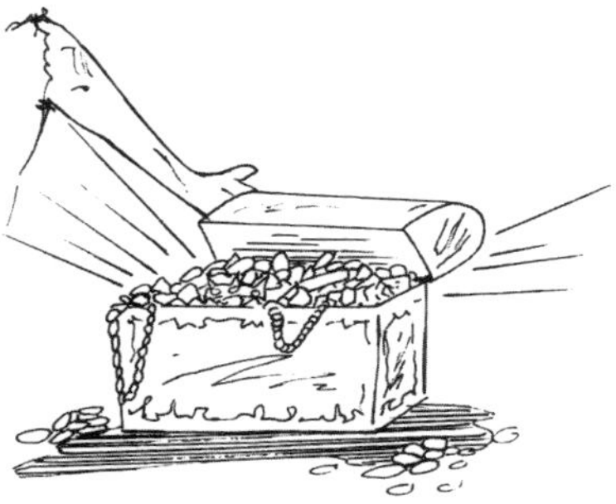

3.

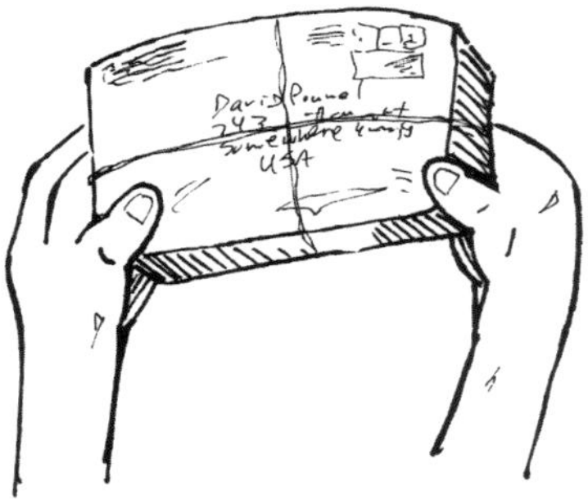

4.

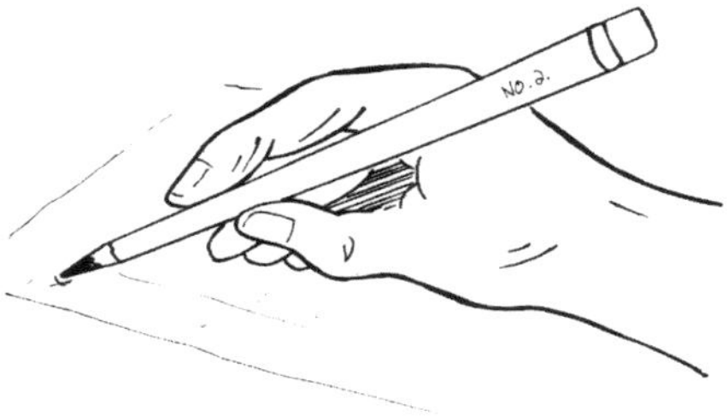

5.

6.

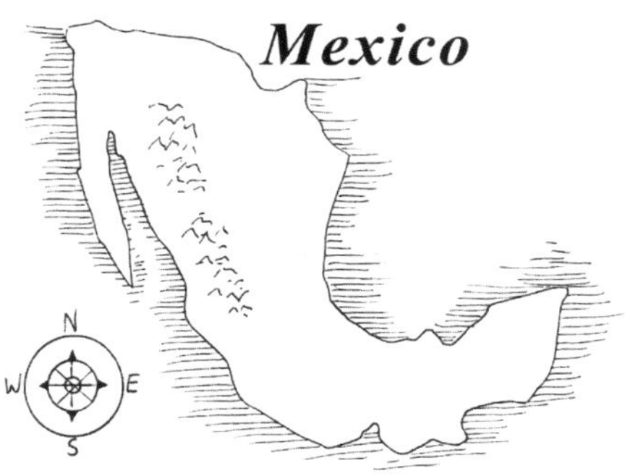

El tiempo

Nombre: ______________________

Fecha: ______________________

Hora: ______________________

Parte 1-En parejas-6 minutos
Take turns saying as many weather expressions as possible.
Use some of these clues: ***hace: viento, sol, calor, frío, buen tiempo, mal tiempo.***

Parte 2-Toda la clase-De pie-14 minutos
Take turns. Introduce yourself as a weather man and give the weather for today in Spanish.
Use some of these clues: ***hace buen tiempo, sol, calor, viento.***

Parte 3-En parejas-6 minutos
Take turns giving the weather for a different city.
Use some of these clues: ***llueve, está, nublado, nieva, hace, mucho frío, hace mucho calor.***

Parte 4-En grupos de cuatro-14 minutos
Make a short rap song using six weather expressions. Sing your song.
Use some of these clues: ***hace calor, hace frío, llueve, nieva, hace viento, hace sol.***

El tiempo

Nombre: ______________________

Fecha: ______________________

Hora: ______________________

Parte 5-En parejas. ¿Qué dices?-10 minutos

1. Look at the drawings below. Describe the weather for each. Say two sentences in Spanish for each drawing. Use some of these clues: ***hace calor, hace frío, nieva, llueve, hace viento, hace sol, hace buen tiempo, hace mal tiempo.***

1.

2.

3.

4.

5.

6.

ALSOP

La comida

Nombre: ______________________

Fecha: ______________________

Hora: ______________________

Parte 1-En parejas-6 minutos
Take turns saying as many foods as possible.
Use some of these clues: ***el pollo, la hamburguesa, la tortilla, el maíz, el flan, la pera, el limón, el café, el agua, la leche.***

Parte 2-Toda la clase-De pie-14 minutos
Take turns. Introduce yourself and tell each student the names of four different foods.
Use some of these clues: ***el pan, los frijoles, el chorizo, la carne de res.***

Parte 3-En parejas-6 minutos
Take turns saying some of the foods as fast as you can.
Use some of these clues: ***el plátano, la naranja, el helado, el pastel, el cordero, el agua.***

Parte 4-En grupos de cuatro-14 minutos
Make a short rock song using foods. Sing your song.
Use some of these clues: ***el helado, las frutas, el café, el pan, las frutas, las verduras, las zanahorias, la lechuga, la carne, el pescado.***

ALSOP

La comida

Nombre: ______________________

Fecha: ______________________

Hora: ______________________

Parte 5-En parejas. ¿Qué dices?-10 minutos

1. Look at the drawing below and say two sentences in Spanish for each drawing. Use some of these clues: ***como, bebo, el café, el helado, el pan, la carne, el plátano, el pollo.***

1.

2.

3.

4.

5.

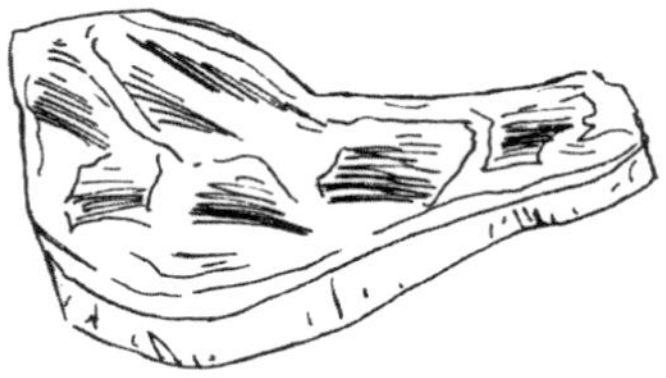

6.

ALSOP

Los números

Nombre: ____________________

Fecha: ____________________

Hora: ____________________

Parte 1-En parejas-6 minutos
Take turns saying the numbers from one to thirty.
Use some of these clues: ***uno, cuatro, siete, ocho, diez, doce, quince, veinete, veintidós, treinta***

Parte 2-Toda la clase-De pie-14 minutos
Take turns. Say the even numbers from one to twenty.
Use some of these clues: ***dos, seis, diez, dieciocho, veinte***

Parte 3-En parejas-6 minutos
Take turns. Make up two addition problems and two substraction problems in Spanish. Use some numbers between one and thirty.
Use some of these clues: ***más (plus), menos (minus), son (equals)***

Parte 4-En grupos de cuatro-14 minutos
Make a short love song using ten numbers between one and thirty. Sing your song.
Use some of these clues: ***uno, ocho, diez, quince, veinete, seis, cuatro, dos, veintiséis, te quiero.***

18-2=16

9-3=6

Los números

Nombre: ____________________

Fecha: ____________________

Hora: ____________________

Parte 5-En parejas. ¿Qué dices?-10 minutos
1. Take turns. Look at the numbers below. Do the addition-substraction problems in Spanish. Use some of these clues: ***más (plus), menos (minus), son (equals), dieciséis, nueve, veinte, trece, quince, veintiuno, catorce.***

1. **18-2=16**
2. **9-3=6**
3. **20-13=7**
4. **15+13=28**
5. **7+7=14**
6. **21+7=28**

ALSOP

Las horas del día

Nombre: ______________________

Fecha: ______________________

Hora: ______________________

Parte 1-En parejas-6 minutos
Take turns saying the following times in Spanish. It is 2:00., It is 6:00., It is 8:00., It is 10:00., It is 4:00., It is 12:00.
Use some of these clues: ***son las dos, son las cuatro.***

Parte 2-Toda la clase-De pie-14 minutos
Take turns. Say what time you study, what time you watch TV, what time you eat, what time you listen to music.
Use some of these clues: ***estudio, miro, como, escucho, a las.***

Parte 3-En parejas-6 minutos
Take turns giving the time in your city, in Madrid, and in Los Ángeles, California. (Add 6-7 hours for Madrid.)
Use some of these clues: ***Son las..... en Madrid.***

Parte 4-En grupos de cuatro-14 minutos
1. Make a short country-music song using six times. Sing your song.
Use some of these clues: ***a las seis, a las ocho, bailo, estudio, canto.***

ALSOP

Las horas del día

Nombre: ____________________

Fecha: ____________________

Hora: ____________________

Parte 5-En parejas. ¿Qué dices?-10 minutos

1. Look at the drawings below. Give the time on each clock. Use some of these clues: ***son las nueve y tres, es la una, son las doce menos veinticinco.***

1.

2.

3.

4.

5.

6.

Los días de la semana

Nombre: ______________________

Fecha: ______________________

Hora: ______________________

Parte 1-En parejas-6 minutos
Take turns saying the days of the week.
Use some of these clues: ***el lunes, el martes, el miércoles, el jueves...***

Parte 2-Toda la clase-De pie-14 minutos
Take turns. Introduce yourself and tell each student the days of the week when you have classes.
Use some of these clues: ***tengo, el lunes, el martes....***

Parte 3-En parejas-6 minutos
Take turns saying the days of the week as fast as you can.
Use some of these clues: ***el lunes, el martes, el jueves.***

Parte 4-En grupos de cuatro-14 minutos
Make a short rap song using the days of the week. Sing your song.
Use some of these clues: ***el lunes, trabajo, el martes, leo, el miércoles,el jueves, el viernes, el sábado, el domingo.***

Los días de la semana

Nombre: ______________________

Fecha: ______________________

Hora: ______________________

Parte 5-En parejas. ¿Qué dices?-10 minutos

1. Look at the drawing below and say what you do and the day you do the activity. Use some of these clues: ***voy a la escuela el lunes, voy a la iglesia el domingo, canto el sábado, bailo el viernes, voy al partido de fútbol el jueves.***

1.

2.

3.

4.

5.

6.

Los colores

Nombre: ______________________

Fecha: ______________________

Hora: ______________________

Parte 1-En parejas-6 minutos
Take turns asking the other his/her favorite colors.
Give at least four colors.
Use these clues: ***¿Cuál es tu color favorito? rojo, blanco, azul, negro, verde, café, amarillo.***

Parte 2-Toda la clase-De pie-14 minutos
Take turns. Tell each class member three colors.
Use some of these clues: ***rojo, azul, negro, gris, verde, amarillo.***

Parte 3-En parejas-8 minutos
Take turns. Say at least six colors as fast as you can.
Use some of these clues: ***violeta, rosado, blanco, morado, rojo, anaranjado.***

Parte 4-En grupos de cuatro-12 minutos
Make a short rock song using the colors. Sing your song.
Use some of these clues: ***azul, blanco, amarillo, verde, rojo, amarillo.***

ALSOP

Los colores

Nombre: ______________________

Fecha: ______________________

Hora: ______________________

Parte 5-En parejas. ¿Qué dices?-10 minutos

1. Take turns Look at the drawing below. Give the color indicated for each object. Use some of these clues: ***la iguana, el perro, la casa, el libro, el coche, el sombrero, es.***

1.

(red)

2.

(pink)

3.

(green)

4.

(black)

5.

(yellow)

6.

(brown)

ALSOP

La ropa

Nombre: ____________________

Fecha: ____________________

Hora: ____________________

Parte 1-En parejas-6 minutos
Take turns saying as many articles of clothing as possible.
Use some of these clues: ***camisa, blusa, pantalones, sombrero, calcetines, cinturón, zapato.***

Parte 2-Toda la clase-De pie-14 minutos
Take turns. Introduce yourself and then say three articles of clothing that you are wearing today.
Use some of these clues: ***me llamo, hoy, llevo (I am wearing), una camisa, una blusa, una falda, etc.***

Parte 3-En parejas-6 minutos
Take turns saying and describing the clothes that each of you are wearing today.
Use some of these clues: ***hoy, usas (you are wearing), una corbata, unos zapatos, una camisa, unos vaqueros.***

Parte 4-En grupos de cuatro-14 minutos
Make a short rap song using six articles of clothing. Sing your song.
Use some of these clues: ***uso, una camisa, unos pantalones, un vestido,un traje de baño, zapatos.***

La ropa

Nombre: ______________________

Fecha: ______________________

Hora: ______________________

Parte 5-En parejas. ¿Qué dices?-10 minutos

1. Look at the drawings below. Describe the clothes in each person. Invent a name for each picture. Give two sentences for each drawing. Use some of these clues: ***usa, pantalones, vaqueros, una camisa, una falda, un vestido, una blusa, zapatos, una corbata un cinturón, un saco, sandalias, un sombrero, abrigo, guantes, cordones, botas.***

1.

2.

3.

4.

5.

6.

La familia

Nombre: ______________________

Fecha: ______________________

Hora: ______________________

Parte 1-En parejas-6 minutos
Take turns telling how many brothers, sisters, aunts and uncles you have.
Use some of these clues: ***tengo, hermanos, hermanas, tíos, tías.***

Parte 2-Toda la clase-De pie-14 minutos
Take turns. Introduce yourself and ask each student how many brothers-sisters he/she has.
Use some of these clues: ***cuántos, tienes, tengo, hermanos, hermanas.***

Parte 3-En parejas-6 minutos
Take turns saying how many cousins and grandparents you have.
Say their names.
Use some of these clues: ***tengo, primos, abuelos, se llama.***

Parte 4-En grupos de cuatro-14 minutos
Make a short rock song using four relatives. Sing your song.
Use some of these clues: ***tengo, hermanos, primos, tíos, abuelos, sobrinos.***

La familia

Nombre: ______________________

Fecha: ______________________

Hora: ______________________

Parte 5-En parejas. ¿Qué dices?-10 minutos

1. Look at the drawing below and say the name of each relative in Spanish. Invent names for each relative. Give two sentences for each drawing. Use some of these clues: ***Pancho es mi tío, María es mi abuela, padre, hermanas, abuelo, primos***. Also, say how many ***padres, abuelos, primos*** that you have. ***clues: tengo.***

1.

2.

3.

4.

5.

6.

El verbo IR y IR A más el infinitivo

Nombre: ______________________

Fecha: ______________________

Hora: ______________________

Parte 1-En parejas-6 minutos
Take turns asking the other if he/she is going to the game, to school, to Mexico, to the dance, to the party, home.
Use these clues: ***vas, al partido, a la fiesta, a la escuela, a México, al baile, a casa.***

Parte 2-Toda la clase-De pie-14 minutos
Take turns. Tell each class member two things you are going to do. Use some of these clues: ***voy a trabajar, voy a bailar, voy a cantar.***

Parte 3-En parejas-8 minutos
Take turns. You role-play a famous celebrity. Give a short speech saying what you are going to do. Say at least four sentences.
Use some of these clues: ***voy a hablar, voy a escuchar, voy a cantar, voy a tocar el piano.***

Parte 4-En grupos de cuatro-12 minutos
Make a short love song saying what your are going to do. Sing your song.
Use one of these clues: ***voy a cantar, voy a decirte, que te quiero, voy a escuchar, voy a bailar, voy a llorar.***

El verbo IR y IR A más el infinitivo

Nombre: ____________________

Fecha: ____________________

Hora: ____________________

Parte 5-En parejas. ¿Qué dices?-10 minutos

1. Take turns Look at the drawing below. Describe what the people are going to do. Give two sentences for each drawing. Invent a name for each person. Use some of these clues: ***va a cantar, va a bailar, va a comer, va a leer, va a dormir, va a escribir***

1.

2.

3.

4.

5.

6.

El verbo TENER

Nombre: ______________________

Fecha: ______________________

Hora: ______________________

Parte 1-En parejas-6 minutos
Take turns conjugating the verb tener. Practice and then conjugate without looking at the clues.
Use some of these clues: ***tengo, tienes, tiene, tenemos, tenéis, tienen.***

Parte 2-Toda la clase-De pie-14 minutos
Take turns. Introduce yourself and then say three things that you have. Use some of these clues: ***me llamo, tengo, un libro, un carro, un amigo, una casa, un hermano.***

Parte 3-En parejas-6 minutos
Take turns saying five things that your friend has.
Use some of these clues: ***tienes, dinero, libros, un carro.***

Parte 4-En grupos de cuatro-14 minutos
Make a short rap song using six things that you have. Sing your song.
Use some of these clues: ***tengo, amigos, un novio, dinero, hermanos, un carro, etc.***

ALSOP

El verbo TENER

Nombre: ______________________

Fecha: ______________________

Hora: ______________________

Parte 5-En parejas. ¿Qué dices?-10 minutos

1. Look at the drawings below. Give two sentences for each drawing. Say what each person has. Give two sentences for each drawing. Invent a name for each person. Use some of these clues: ***dinero, una casa, amigos, libros, una pluma, hermanos, hermanas.***

1.

2.

3.

4.

5.

6.

ALSOP

Nombre: ______________________

Fecha: ______________________

Hora: ______________________

El verbo SER

Parte 1-En parejas-6 minutos
Take turns saying what you and your friend are like.
Use some of these clues: ***soy, eres, guapo, guapa, inteligente, rico, rica, alto, alta.***

Parte 2-Toda la clase-De pie-14 minutos
Take turns. Introduce yourself. Ask your friend what he/she is like. Use some of these clues: ***me llamo, cómo, eres, soy, rico, rica, inteligente, pobre, guapo, guapa, alto, alta, bajo, baja, trabajador, trabajadora.***

Parte 3-En parejas-6 minutos
Take turns saying what profession your relatives are.
Use some of these clues: ***mi padre, es, doctor, dentista, mecánico, plomero, madre, enfermera, profesora, arquitecta.***

Parte 4-En grupos de cuatro-14 minutos
Make a short rock song using the verb ser. Sing your song.
Use some of these clues: ***soy eres, alto, alta, guapo, guapa, rico, rica, inteligente, alumno, alumna.***

ALSOP

El verbo SER

Nombre: ______________________

Fecha: ______________________

Hora: ______________________

Parte 5-En parejas. ¿Qué dices?-10 minutos

1. Look at the drawing below and say what each person is like. Invent names for each person. Give two sentences for each drawing. Use some of these clues: ***Pablo es alto, María es guapa, es rico, es bajo, es inteligente, es pobre.***

1.

2.

3.

4.

5.

6.

ALSOP

El verbo ESTAR

Nombre: ____________________

Fecha: ____________________

Hora: ____________________

Parte 1-En parejas-6 minutos
Take turns asking the other if he/she is sick, sad, tired, happy, or bored.
Use these clues: ***estás, enfermo, enferma, triste, cansado, cansada, contento, contenta, aburrido, aburrida.***

Parte 2-Toda la clase-De pie-14 minutos
Take turns. Tell each class member where your parents are.
Use some of these clues: ***mis padres, están, en casa, en su trabajo, de vacaciones.***

Parte 3-En parejas-8 minutos
Take turns. You role-play a famous celebrity. Give a short TV commercial saying how you are. Say at least four sentences.
Use some of these clues: ***estoy, cansado, cansada, enfermo, enferma, triste, contento, contenta.***

Parte 4-En grupos de cuatro-12 minutos
Make a short love song saying how you are. Sing your song.
Use one of these clues: ***estoy, contento, contenta, triste, cansado, cansada, enfermo, enferma, aburrido, aburrida, sin ti.***

ALSOP

El verbo ESTAR

Nombre: ______________________

Fecha: ______________________

Hora: ______________________

Parte 5-En parejas. ¿Qué dices?-10 minutos

1. Take turns Look at the drawing below. Describe how each person is or where the person is. Invent a name for each person. Give two sentences for each drawing. Use some of these clues: ***María está enferma, está triste, está contenta, está aburrido, está cansado, en México, en la escuela.***

1.

2.

3.

4.

5.

6.

Los verbos de cambio de raíz

Nombre: ______________________

Fecha: ______________________

Hora: ______________________

Parte 1–En parejas–6 minutos
Take turns saying two things you want to do and two things you can do.
Use some of these clues: ***quiero, puedo, trabajar, estudiar, comer, ir, vivir, en, escribir, descansar.***

Parte 2–Toda la clase–De pie–14 minutos
Take turns. Introduce yourself and then say one thing you want to do and one thing you can do.
Use some of these clues: ***me llamo, quiero, puedo, estudiar, aprender, escribir, vivir, jugar, cocinar.***

Parte 3–En parejas–6 minutos
Take turns asking each other what each wants to do and what each can do.
Use some of these clues: ***quieres, puedes, trabajar, estudiar, bailar, cantar, comer, vivir, en, salir, aprender, hablar.***

Parte 4–En grupos de cuatro–14 minutos
Make a short rap song using the verbs *querer* and *poder.* Sing your song.
Use some of these clues: ***puedo, quiero, puedes, quieres, puede, quiere, podemos, queremos, podéis, queréis, pueden, quieren.***

ALSOP

Los verbos de cambio de raíz

Nombre: ____________________

Fecha: ____________________

Hora: ____________________

Parte 5-En parejas. ¿Qué dices?-10 minutos

1. Look at the drawings below. Describe what each person can do and what each wants to do. Invent a name for each person. Give two sentences for each drawing. Use some of these clues: ***puede, quiere, bailar, cantar, comer, abrir, dormir, viajar.***

1.

2.

3.

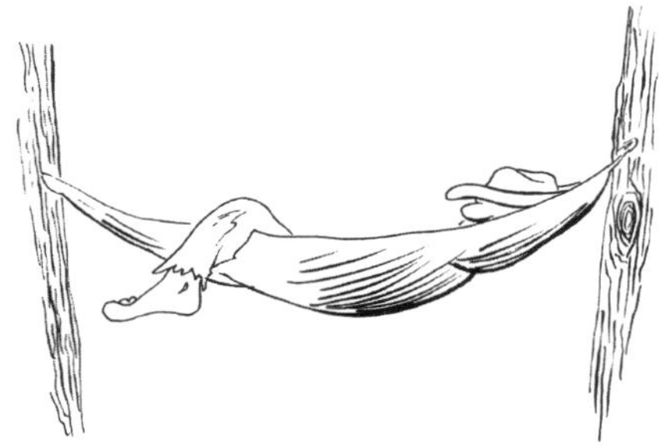

4.

5.

6.

El verbo GUSTAR

Nombre: ______________________

Fecha: ______________________

Hora: ______________________

Parte 1-En parejas-6 minutos
Take turns saying what you like.
Use some of these clues: ***me gusta, me gustan, mi libro, el reloj, mi novio, mi novia, mis libros, tus libros, los zapatos.***

Parte 2-Toda la clase-De pie-14 minutos
Take turns. Introduce yourself and ask each student what he/she likes.
Each student is to ask and answer the question.
Use some of these clues: ***te gusta, sí, me gusta, te gustan, me gustan, mis clases, mis profesores, mi casa, mi novio.***

Parte 3-En parejas-6 minutos
Take turns saying what you do not like.
Use some of these clues: ***no me gusta, no me gustan, mis clases, mi tía, mi abuela, España, mi profesora, mi profesor.***

Parte 4-En grupos de cuatro-14 minutos
Make a short rock song using four things you like. Sing your song.
Use some of these clues: ***me gusta, me gustan, mi perro, mi gato, mi madre, mi padre, mis clases, mi novio, mi novia.***

Nombre: ______________________

Fecha: ______________________

Hora: ______________________

El verbo GUSTAR

Parte 5-En parejas. ¿Qué dices?-10 minutos

1. Look at the drawing below and say what each person or animal likes. Invent names for each person or animal. Use some of these clues: ***A Marisol le gusta la casa, le gusta, le gustan, el helado, el carro, el perro, alos gatos, a los muchachos.***

1.

2.

3.

4.

5.

6.

Los modismos con TENER

Nombre: ____________________

Fecha: ____________________

Hora: ____________________

Parte 1-En parejas-6 minutos
Take turns asking the other if he/she is sleepy, hungry, thirsty, lucky, afraid.
Use these clues: tienes, sed, hambre, miedo, suerte.

Parte 2-Toda la clase-De pie-14 minutos
Take turns. Use five tener idioms to describe how you are.
Use some of these clues: ***tengo, sueño, sed, calor, frío, hambre, sueño, suerte, miedo.***

Parte 3-En parejas-8 minutos
Take turns. You role-play a famous celebrity. Give a short TV commercial saying how you are after taking a new medicine. Say at least four sentences.
Use some of these clues: ***después de, tomar, medicina, tengo sueño, sed, hambre, miedo, prisa, calor, frió, ay de mí.***

Parte 4-En grupos de cuatro-12 minutos
Make a short love song using tener idioms. Sing your song.
Use one of these clues: ***tengo, frío, calor, hambre, prisa, sed, razón, suerte, sueño, miedo, al pensar, en ti.***

Los modismos con TENER

Nombre: ______________________

Fecha: ______________________

Hora: ______________________

Parte 5-En parejas. ¿Qué dices?-10 minutos

Take turns Look at the drawing below. Describe the people using a tener idiom. Invent a name for each person. Give two sentences for each drawing. Use some of these clues: ***tiene, sueño, sed, calor, frío, miedo, prisa, suerte.***

1.

2.

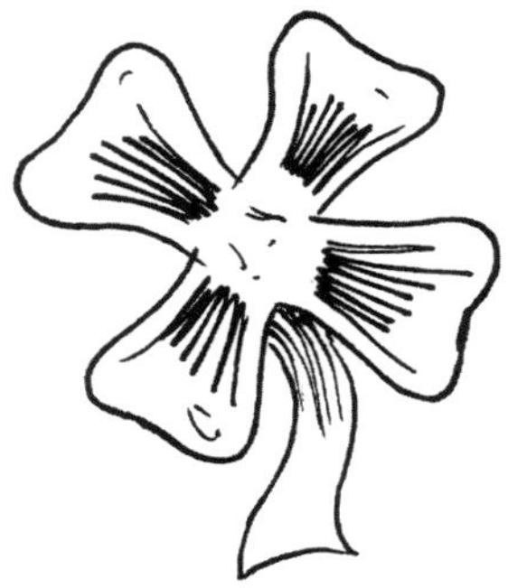

3.

4.

5.

6.

Los complementos directos

Nombre: ____________________

Fecha: ____________________

Hora: ____________________

Parte 1-En parejas-6 minutos
Take turns saying the direct object pronouns. Say the pronouns the second time without looking at the clues.
Use some of these clues: ***me, te, lo, la, le, nos, os, los, las.***

Parte 2-Toda la clase-De pie-14 minutos
Take turns. Introduce yourself and then use two direct object pronouns to say what you are reading and what you are looking for.
Use some of these clues: ***lo leo, la leo, lo busco.***

Parte 3-En parejas-6 minutos
Use two direct object pronouns to describe what your friend is selling.
Use some of these clues: ***vendes, lo, la, los, las.***

Parte 4-En grupos de cuatro-14 minutos
Make a short rap song using the direct object pronouns. Sing your song.
Use some of these clues: ***me, te, le, lo, la, nos, os, los, las.***

ALSOP

Los complementos directos

Nombre: ______________________

Fecha: ______________________

Hora: ______________________

Parte 5-En parejas. ¿Qué dices?-10 minutos

1. Look at the drawings below. Say what each person is selling using a direct object pronoun. Give two sentences for each drawing. Invent a name for each person. Use some of these clues: ***la vende, lo vende, los vende, las vende.***

1.

2.

3.

4.

5.

6.

ALSOP

Los complementos indirectos

Nombre: ____________________

Fecha: ____________________

Hora: ____________________

Parte 1-En parejas-6 minutos
Take turns saying the indirect object pronouns. Say the pronouns the second time without looking at the clues.
Use some of these clues: ***me, te, le, nos, os, les***

Parte 2-Toda la clase-De pie-14 minutos
Take turns. Introduce yourself and then use two indirect object pronouns to say to whom you are giving the book.
Use some of these clues: ***te, le, les, el libro, doy***

Parte 3-En parejas-6 minutos
Use two indirect object pronouns to say to whom you are writing the letter.
Use some of these clues: ***escribo, te, le, les.***

Parte 4-En grupos de cuatro-14 minutos
Make a short rock song using the indirect object pronouns with two verbs. Sing your song.
Use some of these clues: ***doy, das, da, me, te, le, nos, os, les***

Los complementos indirectos

Nombre: ______________________

Fecha: ______________________

Hora: ______________________

Parte 5-En parejas. ¿Qué dices?-10 minutos
1. Look at the drawings below. Say what each picture is giving and to whom using an indirect object pronoun. Invent a person to go with each picutre. Use some of these clues: ***le da, un regalo, dinero, un perro, flores, cinco peces, un collar.***

1.

2.

3.

4.

5.

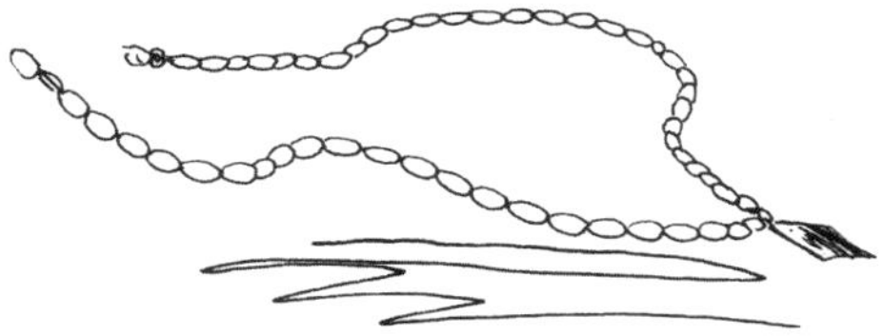

6.

Los sustantivos y los adjetivos

Nombre: ______________________

Fecha: ______________________

Hora: ______________________

Parte 1-En parejas-6 minutos
Take turns describing the other using four nouns and four adjectives.
Use these clues: el muchacho, la muchacho(a), es, alto, alta, inteligente, el estudiante, la estudiante, guapo, guapa.

Parte 2-Toda la clase-De pie-14 minutos
Take turns. Describe three of your relatives in Spanish.
Use some of these clues: ***mis, tíos, mexicanos, son, abuelos, ricos, padres, guapos.***

Parte 3-En parejas-8 minutos
Take turns. You role-play a famous celebrity. Give a short speech describing your family using nouns and adjectives. Say four sentences.
Use some of these clues: ***mi, hermano, hermana, es, española, primos, son, pobres, madre, guapa, sincera, padre, honrado.***

Parte 4-En grupos de cuatro-12 minutos
Make up a love song about your friends using nouns and adjectives. Sing your song.
Use some of these clues: ***mis amigos, sinceros, son, simpáticos, quiero, a mis amigos***

ALSOP

Los sustantivos y los adjetivos

Nombre: ______________________

Fecha: ______________________

Hora: ______________________

Parte 5-En parejas. ¿Qué dices?-10 minutos
Take turns Look at the drawing below. Describe the people using nouns and adjectives. Use some of these clues: ***la muchacha, alta, es, el muchacho, guapo, simpática, el hombre, bajo.***

1.

2.

3.

4.

5.

6.

Las expresiones negativas

Parte 1-En parejas-6 minutos
Take turns saying as many negative expressions as possible.
Use some of these clues: ***nada, nadie, nunca, ni..ni***

Parte 2-Toda la clase-De pie-14 minutos
Take turns. Say two sentences using negative expressions.
Use some of these clues: ***no hay nada, na hay nadie, en casa, no estudio nunca.***

Parte 3-En parejas-6 minutos
Take turns and tell each other that you never study, there is nothing on the table, and no one listens.
Use some of these clues: ***nadie, escucha, estudia, nunca, nada, no hay, en la mesa.***

Parte 4-En grupos de cuatro-14 minutos
Make a short rap song using four negative expressions. Sing your song.
Use some of these clues: ***no canto, nunca, no bailo, no escucho, a nadie, no escribo, nada.***

Nombre: ______________________

Fecha: ______________________

Hora: ______________________

Las expresiones negativas

Parte 5-En parejas. ¿Qué dices?-10 minutos

1. Look at the drawings below. Describe what eas person does not do using an appropriate negative word. Invent a name for each person. Use some of these clues: ***nunca, nada, escucha, trabaja, come, estudia, corre, baila.***

1.

2.

3.

4.

5.

6.

ALSOP

Nombre: ______________________

Fecha: ______________________

Hora: ______________________

El verbo TENER QUE más el infinitivo

Parte 1-En parejas-6 minutos
Take turns saying what you have to do.
Use some of these clues: ***tengo que, trabajar, escuchar, bailar, salir, aprender, preparar, la comida.***

Parte 2-Toda la clase-De pie-14 minutos
Take turns. Introduce yourself and ask each student what he/she has to do. Use some of these clues: ***tienes que, jugar, dormir, estudiar, descansar, comer.***

Parte 3-En parejas-6 minutos
Take turns saying what your brother or sister has to do.
Use some of these clues: ***mi, hermano, hermana, tiene que, trabajar, ir, al cine, salir, vivir, España, comer, correr, abrir, la puerta.***

Parte 4-En grupos de cuatro-14 minutos
Make a short rock song saying what you have to do. Sing your song.
Use some of these clues: ***tengo que, jugar, tocar, banda, bailar, cantar, escuchar, música. ir, a comer***.

ALSOP

El verbo TENER QUE más el infinitivo

Nombre: ______________________

Fecha: ______________________

Hora: ______________________

Parte 5-En parejas. ¿Qué dices?-10 minutos

1. Look at the drawing below and say what each person has to do. Invent names for each. Use some of these clues: ***tiene que, viajar, descansar, aprender, correr, cocinar, bailar.***

1.

2.

3.

4.

5.

6.

ALSOP